This book belongs to

AYDEN

you are love

Always remember who you are ... ♡
With so much love~ From Mimi
6-3-20

love

a story about who you truly are.

By: Anita Moorjani   and   Angie DeMuro

First Edition – September 2017

ISBN 978-0-9885568-8-1

Editor: Douglas Burak
Book set up: Douglas Burak
Design: Angie DeMuro

This book is hand lettered by Angie DeMuro.
Illustrations were drawn with pencil on 140 lb watercolor paper and
hand colored using opaque watercolor paints,
pen and ink and markers.

Distributed by Nick of Time Printing LLC
Manufactured by Create Space

Nick of Time Printing LLC
2937 Memorial Highway
Dallas, PA. 18612
www.nickoftimeprinting.com

This book is
dedicated to
YOU,
and you are
LOVE ♥

Love,
Anita and Angie

Hi, my name is

Anita

I love you!
I really do!

do you know why?

Because you are me

and I am you.

We are all the same.

Our bodies may look different on the outside.

But our outsides are not who we truly are.

We are really energy,

and that energy is Love

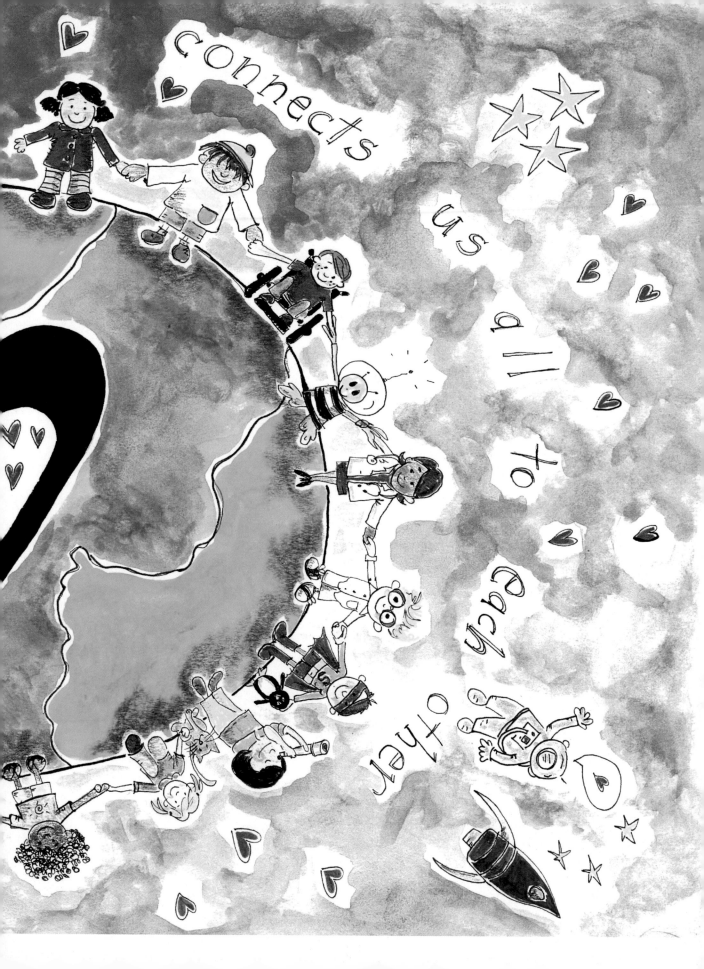

Love is not something you can see or hear. It is something you can FEEL.

When your mom or dad gives you a big hug and you hug back with all of your might! That is the FEELING of Love being shared.

But before we can share love with others, we must give it to ourselves first.

How do you do that?

Self LOVE

Be your own
best friend.

Love
Yourself
just as you
are!

Even when
you are
Sick.

Or get a low grade
in school.

Or make
a
bad choice.

Just love yourself

through it.
Self Soothe

Because when you love 🖤 yourself you realize that you are Magnificent !

And that you can do anything that comes your way. Because, after all you are

Magnificent !

When you love yourself it's so
easy to share that love with others.

Smile at someone and watch
them smile back at you.

Share your toy
with them.

Go over to someone
sitting all alone
and say,

You are
connecting
your energy
with theirs.

You are sharing love.

Love is super
Portable.
You can take it with
you everywhere
you go.

And share it with everyone you meet.

SPREAD
love around.

You can add a bit
of love to all you do!

Brushing
You
teeth

eating your
lunch

Cooking
dinner

even
cleaning
Your room

Now listen,
    There may be times
when people will do or say
things that will make you
think that love is
    not around.

Love can never leave you.
It's always with you,
because
YOU
are
LOVE !

That is why there is nothing you can say or do to make yourself unlovable.

All you have to do is be as
You as you can be,

and love yourself
for all that you
are!

33

Age 5

Anita Moorjani is the author of two books: "Dying to be Me - My journey from cancer to near death to true healing" and "What if This is Heaven." She was born in Singapore of Indian parents, moved to Hong Kong at the age of two, and has lived in Hong Kong most of her life. Because of her background and British education, she is multi lingual and, from the age of two, grew up speaking English, Cantonese and an Indian dialect simultaneously. She had been working in the corporate field for several years before being diagnosed with cancer in April of 2002. Her fascinating and moving near-death experience in early 2006 has tremendously changed her perspective on life. Her life is now ingrained with the depths and insights she gained while in the other realm.

As a result of her near death experience, Anita is often invited to speak at conferences and events to share her insights. She is also a frequent speaker at universities, particularly for their department of behavioral sciences, speaking on topics such as: dealing with terminal illness; facing death; psychology of spiritual beliefs; etc. She is the embodiment of the truth that we all have the inner power and wisdom to overcome even life's most adverse situations, as she is the living proof of this possibility. Anita and her husband Danny live part of the time in the United States, and part of the time in Hong Kong.

You may visit her here www.anitamorjani.com

Age 5

Angie DeMuro is a children's author, illustrator and cartoonist. She has currently written, illustrated and published seven books and one angel and fairy oracle deck and guide book. Her comics, illustrated recipes and illustrations have been published nationally.

Angie's comic strip "Life with Mr. M." can be read regularly in Autism Parenting Magazine and Autism Asperger's Digest. The comic strip was inspired by Angie's youngest son, who in 2012 was diagnosed with Asperger's Syndrome, (a high functioning form of Autism).

Angie is attuned to the Master level of Usui Shiki Ryoho Reiki Method of Natural Healing, attuned to the Advanced Level of Integrated Energy Therapy® system, a Master Teacher in Magnified Healing®, attuned to Angel Healing® Level I and a Spiritual Medium and intuitive artist, teacher and positive speaker.

Angie is the proud mom of three sons, two of whom are grown. She resides in a cozy farmhouse located in Northeastern Pennsylvania with her husband Douglas, two youngest sons and their silly dog named Bigsley.

You may visit her here www.angiedemuro.com

The *love* yourself pledge

I _____
(your name Here)

♥ I pledge to always |LOVE| myself no matter what, through good times and not so good times.

♥ I pledge to |ALways| be my own best friend.

♥ I pledge to stand up for myself and to always be kind to myself.

♥ I pledge to never criticize myself.

♥ I pledge to say nice things to and about myself.

♥ I pledge to always be as |ME| as I can be.

♥ I pledge to never dim my light for anyone, ever.

I Love myself forever!

Made in the USA
Columbia, SC
30 May 2020